MY KITCHEN RECIPE COLLECTION

PULTENEY
PRESS

First published by Pulteney Press in 2017
Copyright © Pulteney Press 2017

Written by Katherine Sully • Illustrated by Frankie Van Mourik

ISBN 978-1-78718-687-3
Printed in China

CONTENTS

USEFUL INFORMATION

WEIGHTS AND MEASURES:

TEASPOONS	TABLESPOONS	GRAMS	OUNCES	MILLILITRES	FLUID OUNCES
3 tsp	1 tbsp	10g	½ oz	10ml	½ fl oz
6 tsp	2 tbsp	25g	1 oz	25ml	1 fl oz
12 tsp	4 tbsp	50g	2 oz	50ml	2 fl oz
16 tsp	5 tbsp	75g	3 oz	75ml	3 fl oz
24 tsp	8 tbsp	110g	4 oz	110ml	4 fl oz
30 tsp	10 tbsp	150g	5 oz	140ml	5 (¼ pint)
36 tsp	12 tbsp	175g	6 oz	275ml	10 (½ pint)
48 tsp	16 tbsp	225g	8 (½ pound)	570ml	1 pint

The above figures are rounded up UK measure conversions.

TEMPERATURES:

°C	°F	GAS
140	275	1
150	300	2
170	325	3
180	350	4
190	375	5
200	400	6

MY READY RECKONER:

2 handfuls of rice = 1 portion of rice per person

SAUCES, SOUPS AND DIPS

Spicy sauces, hearty soups and delicious dips. Putting some zip and zest into food for casual sharing can be fun and exciting. Experimenting with basic recipes adds an element of suprise. Often, its those ingredients (forgotten at the back of the fridge!) added at the last minute that can lift a reliable standard to a whole new level.

RECIPE FINDER

Place your recipe photo here.

RECIPE:

SERVES: _____   PREP TIME: _____

OVEN TEMP: _____   COOKING TIME: _____

INGREDIENTS:

_____   _____

_____   _____

_____   _____

_____   _____

_____   _____

_____   _____

_____   _____

METHOD:

_____

_____

_____

_____

_____

_____

_____

_____

Tips & Suggestions:

RECIPE:

SERVES: _____

OVEN TEMP: _____

PREP TIME: _____

COOKING TIME: _____

INGREDIENTS:

_____ _____

_____ _____

_____ _____

_____ _____

_____ _____

_____ _____

_____ _____

Place your recipe photo here.

METHOD:

_____

_____

_____

_____

_____

_____

_____

_____

_____

_____

_____

_____

_____

_____

_____

_____

_____

_____

_____

_____

_____

_____

_____

Tips & Suggestions:

RECIPE:

SERVES:

OVEN TEMP:

PREP TIME:

COOKING TIME:

INGREDIENTS:

METHOD:

Place your recipe photo here.

Tips & Suggestions:

RECIPE:

SERVES: _____   PREP TIME: _____

OVEN TEMP: _____   COOKING TIME: _____

INGREDIENTS:

_____   _____

_____   _____

_____   _____

_____   _____

_____   _____

_____   _____

Place your recipe photo here.

METHOD:

_____

_____

_____

_____

_____

_____

_____

_____

_____

Tips & Suggestions:

Place your recipe photo here.

RECIPE:

SERVES: _____   PREP TIME: _____

OVEN TEMP: _____   COOKING TIME: _____

INGREDIENTS:

_____   _____
_____   _____
_____   _____
_____   _____
_____   _____
_____   _____
_____   _____

METHOD:

_____
_____
_____
_____
_____
_____
_____

Tips & Suggestions:

RECIPE:

SERVES: _____ PREP TIME: _____

OVEN TEMP: _____ COOKING TIME: _____

INGREDIENTS:

_____ _____

_____ _____

_____ _____

_____ _____

_____ _____

_____ _____

_____

METHOD:

_____

_____

_____

_____

_____

_____

_____

_____

_____

_____

_____

_____

_____

_____

_____

_____

_____

_____

_____

_____

_____

Place your recipe
photo here.

Tips & Suggestions:

RECIPE:

SERVES: _____   PREP TIME: _____

OVEN TEMP: _____   COOKING TIME: _____

INGREDIENTS:

_____   _____

_____   _____

_____   _____

_____   _____

_____   _____

_____   _____

_____

Place your recipe photo here.

METHOD:

_____

_____

_____

_____

_____

_____

_____

_____

_____

_____

_____

_____

_____

_____

_____

_____

_____

_____

_____

_____

_____

_____

Tips & Suggestions:

STARTERS AND SIDE DISHES

Salads and nibbles, pâtés and platters, sautéed, roasted and deep fried veg. Starters set the tone for the rest of the meal and buy precious time before the main meal is ready to be served. Side dishes compliment the main dish. It's good to have a few quick and easy recipes for those impulsive moments when everyone is invited back to yours!

Recipe Finder

Place your recipe photo here.

RECIPE:

SERVES: _____

PREP TIME: _____

OVEN TEMP: _____

COOKING TIME: _____

INGREDIENTS:

_____ _____

_____ _____

_____ _____

_____ _____

_____ _____

_____ _____

_____ _____

METHOD:

_____

_____

_____

_____

_____

_____

_____

_____

Tips & Suggestions:

RECIPE:

SERVES: _____ PREP TIME: _____

OVEN TEMP: _____ COOKING TIME: _____

INGREDIENTS:

_____ _____

_____ _____

_____ _____

_____ _____

_____ _____

METHOD:

_____

_____

_____

_____

_____

_____

_____

_____

_____

_____

_____

_____

_____

_____

_____

_____

Place your recipe
photo here.

Tips & Suggestions:

RECIPE:

SERVES:

PREP TIME:

OVEN TEMP:

COOKING TIME:

INGREDIENTS:

METHOD:

Place your recipe
photo here.

Tips & Suggestions:

RECIPE:

SERVES: _____   PREP TIME: _____

OVEN TEMP: _____   COOKING TIME: _____

INGREDIENTS:

_____   _____

_____   _____

_____   _____

_____   _____

_____   _____

_____   _____

Place your recipe photo here.

METHOD:

_____

_____

_____

_____

_____

_____

_____

_____

Tips & Suggestions:

Place your recipe
photo here.

RECIPE:

SERVES: _____   PREP TIME: _____

OVEN TEMP: _____   COOKING TIME: _____

INGREDIENTS:

_____	_____
_____	_____
_____	_____
_____	_____
_____	_____
_____	_____

METHOD:

_____

_____

_____

_____

_____

_____

Tips & Suggestions:

RECIPE:

SERVES: _____ PREP TIME: _____

OVEN TEMP: _____ COOKING TIME: _____

INGREDIENTS:

_____ _____
_____ _____
_____ _____
_____ _____
_____ _____
_____ _____

Place your recipe photo here.

METHOD:

_____
_____
_____
_____
_____
_____
_____
_____
_____
_____
_____
_____
_____
_____
_____
_____
_____

Tips & Suggestions:

RECIPE:

SERVES: _____ PREP TIME: _____

OVEN TEMP: _____ COOKING TIME: _____

INGREDIENTS:

_____ _____

_____ _____

_____ _____

_____ _____

_____ _____

_____ _____

Place your recipe photo here.

METHOD:

_____

_____

_____

_____

_____

_____

_____

_____

_____

_____

_____

_____

_____

_____

_____

_____

_____

_____

_____

Tips & Suggestions:

MAIN DISHES

Pot roast, oven roast, tray bakes, curries, stir fries, pies, pizzas, pastas, risottos and paellas. The main part of the meal provides the nourishment, food to be lingered over with friends and family. Tried and tested dishes are a lifesaver for the busy cook. They give you the confidence to relax and enjoy the company.

RECIPE FINDER

Place your recipe photo here.

RECIPE:

SERVES: PREP TIME:

OVEN TEMP: COOKING TIME:

INGREDIENTS:

METHOD:

Tips & Suggestions:

RECIPE:

SERVES: _____   PREP TIME: _____

OVEN TEMP: _____   COOKING TIME: _____

INGREDIENTS:

METHOD:

Place your recipe
photo here.

Tips & Suggestions:

RECIPE:

SERVES: _____   PREP TIME: _____

OVEN TEMP: _____   COOKING TIME: _____

INGREDIENTS:

_____   _____

_____   _____

_____   _____

_____   _____

_____   _____

_____   _____

Place your recipe
photo here.

METHOD:

_____

_____

_____

_____

_____

_____

_____

_____

_____

_____

_____

_____

_____

_____

_____

_____

_____

_____

_____

_____

_____

Tips & Suggestions:

RECIPE:

SERVES: _____   PREP TIME: _____

OVEN TEMP: _____   COOKING TIME: _____

INGREDIENTS:

_____   _____

_____   _____

_____   _____

_____   _____

_____   _____

Place your recipe photo here.

METHOD:

_____

_____

_____

_____

_____

_____

_____

Tips & Suggestions:

Place your recipe photo here.

RECIPE:

SERVES: _____   PREP TIME: _____

OVEN TEMP: _____   COOKING TIME: _____

INGREDIENTS:

METHOD:

Tips & Suggestions:

RECIPE:

SERVES: _____ PREP TIME: _____

OVEN TEMP: _____ COOKING TIME: _____

INGREDIENTS:

_____
_____
_____
_____
_____
_____
_____

Place your recipe
photo here.

METHOD:

_____
_____
_____
_____
_____
_____
_____
_____
_____
_____
_____
_____
_____
_____
_____
_____
_____
_____
_____
_____

Tips & Suggestions:

RECIPE:

SERVES: _____ PREP TIME: _____

OVEN TEMP: _____ COOKING TIME: _____

INGREDIENTS:

_____ _____

_____ _____

_____ _____

_____ _____

_____ _____

_____ _____

Place your recipe photo here.

METHOD:

_____

_____

_____

_____

_____

_____

_____

_____

_____

_____

_____

_____

_____

_____

_____

_____

_____

_____

_____

_____

Tips & Suggestions:

RECIPE:

SERVES:

PREP TIME:

OVEN TEMP:

COOKING TIME:

INGREDIENTS:

Place your recipe photo here.

METHOD:

Tips & Suggestions:

Place your recipe photo here.

RECIPE:

SERVES: _____ PREP TIME: _____

OVEN TEMP: _____ COOKING TIME: _____

INGREDIENTS:

_____ _____

_____ _____

_____ _____

_____ _____

_____ _____

METHOD:

_____

_____

_____

_____

_____

_____

_____

Tips & Suggestions:

RECIPE:

SERVES: PREP TIME:

OVEN TEMP: COOKING TIME:

INGREDIENTS:

METHOD:

Place your recipe
photo here.

Tips & Suggestions:

RECIPE:

SERVES: _____   PREP TIME: _____

OVEN TEMP: _____   COOKING TIME: _____

INGREDIENTS:

_____   _____

_____   _____

_____   _____

_____   _____

_____   _____

_____   _____

_____   _____

_____   _____

Place your recipe photo here.

METHOD:

_____

_____

_____

_____

_____

_____

_____

_____

_____

_____

_____

_____

_____

_____

_____

_____

_____

_____

_____

_____

_____

_____

Tips & Suggestions:

RECIPE:

SERVES: _____   PREP TIME: _____

OVEN TEMP: _____   COOKING TIME: _____

INGREDIENTS:

_____   _____

_____   _____

_____   _____

_____   _____

_____   _____

_____   _____

Place your recipe photo here.

METHOD:

_____

_____

_____

_____

_____

_____

_____

_____

_____

_____

Tips & Suggestions:

Place your recipe photo here.

RECIPE:

SERVES: _____ PREP TIME: _____

OVEN TEMP: _____ COOKING TIME: _____

INGREDIENTS:

METHOD:

Tips & Suggestions:

RECIPE:

SERVES: _____ PREP TIME: _____

OVEN TEMP: _____ COOKING TIME: _____

INGREDIENTS:

_____ _____

_____ _____

_____ _____

_____ _____

_____ _____

METHOD:

_____

_____

_____

_____

_____

_____

_____

_____

_____

_____

_____

_____

_____

_____

_____

Place your recipe photo here.

Tips & Suggestions:

RECIPE:

SERVES: _____   PREP TIME: _____

OVEN TEMP: _____   COOKING TIME: _____

INGREDIENTS:

_____   _____

_____   _____

_____   _____

_____   _____

_____   _____

_____   _____

METHOD:

_____
_____
_____
_____
_____
_____
_____
_____
_____
_____
_____
_____
_____
_____
_____
_____
_____
_____
_____
_____

Place your recipe photo here.

Tips & Suggestions:

PUDDINGS AND PASTRIES

Tarts and trifles, jellies and custards, meringues and mousses, ice creams and sorbets, puddings and pastries. This can be time to show off creative skills and artistic temperament. It can also be the moment to bring out traditional favourites, comfort puddings remembered from childhood, a link with other cooks and kitchens from days gone by.

Recipe Finder

Place your recipe
photo here.

RECIPE:

SERVES: PREP TIME:

OVEN TEMP: COOKING TIME:

INGREDIENTS:

METHOD:

Tips & Suggestions:

RECIPE:

SERVES:

OVEN TEMP:

PREP TIME:

COOKING TIME:

INGREDIENTS:

METHOD:

Place your recipe
photo here.

Tips & Suggestions:

RECIPE:

SERVES: _____ PREP TIME: _____

OVEN TEMP: _____ COOKING TIME: _____

INGREDIENTS:

_____ _____
_____ _____
_____ _____
_____ _____
_____ _____
_____ _____

Place your recipe photo here.

METHOD:

_____
_____
_____
_____
_____
_____
_____
_____
_____
_____
_____
_____
_____
_____
_____
_____
_____
_____
_____
_____

Tips & Suggestions:

RECIPE:

SERVES: _____   PREP TIME: _____

OVEN TEMP: _____   COOKING TIME: _____

INGREDIENTS:

_____   _____

_____   _____

_____   _____

_____   _____

_____   _____

Place your recipe photo here.

METHOD:

_____

_____

_____

_____

_____

_____

_____

_____

Tips & Suggestions:

Place your recipe photo here.

RECIPE:

SERVES: _____   PREP TIME: _____

OVEN TEMP: _____   COOKING TIME: _____

INGREDIENTS:

_____   _____

_____   _____

_____   _____

_____   _____

_____   _____

_____   _____

METHOD:

_____

_____

_____

_____

_____

_____

_____

_____

_____

Tips & Suggestions:

RECIPE:

SERVES: _____   PREP TIME: _____

OVEN TEMP: _____   COOKING TIME: _____

INGREDIENTS:

_____   _____

_____   _____

_____   _____

_____   _____

_____   _____

_____   _____

METHOD:

_____

_____

_____

_____

_____

_____

_____

_____

_____

_____

_____

_____

_____

_____

_____

_____

_____

_____

_____

_____

_____

Place your recipe photo here.

Tips & Suggestions:

RECIPE:

SERVES:

PREP TIME:

OVEN TEMP:

COOKING TIME:

INGREDIENTS:

METHOD:

Place your recipe photo here.

Tips & Suggestions:

RECIPE:

SERVES: PREP TIME:

OVEN TEMP: COOKING TIME:

INGREDIENTS:

Place your recipe photo here.

METHOD:

Tips & Suggestions:

RECIPE:

Serves: _____ Prep time: _____

Oven temp: _____ Cooking time: _____

INGREDIENTS:

_____ _____
_____ _____
_____ _____
_____ _____
_____ _____
_____ _____

Place your recipe photo here.

METHOD:

_____
_____
_____
_____
_____
_____
_____
_____
_____
_____
_____
_____
_____
_____
_____
_____
_____
_____
_____

Tips & Suggestions:

CAKES AND BISCUITS

Fruit cakes, sponge cakes, layer cakes, cheesecakes, cupcakes, tray bakes, cookies and scones. Everyone has a favourite. There are simple cakes for fundraisers, everyday cakes for tea and coffee breaks, and then there are the elaborate, special occasion cakes that have stories, photos and precious memories attached.

Recipe Finder

Place your recipe photo here.

RECIPE:

SERVES: _____ PREP TIME: _____

OVEN TEMP: _____ COOKING TIME: _____

INGREDIENTS:

_____ _____

_____ _____

_____ _____

_____ _____

_____ _____

_____ _____

METHOD:

_____

_____

_____

_____

_____

_____

_____

_____

Tips & Suggestions:

RECIPE:

SERVES: _____ PREP TIME: _____

OVEN TEMP: _____ COOKING TIME: _____

INGREDIENTS:

_____ _____

_____ _____

_____ _____

_____ _____

_____ _____

_____ _____

Place your recipe photo here.

METHOD:

_____

_____

_____

_____

_____

_____

_____

_____

_____

_____

_____

_____

_____

_____

_____

_____

_____

_____

Tips & Suggestions:

RECIPE:

SERVES: _____   PREP TIME: _____

OVEN TEMP: _____   COOKING TIME: _____

INGREDIENTS:

_____   _____

_____   _____

_____   _____

_____   _____

_____   _____

_____   _____

Place your recipe photo here.

METHOD:

_____

_____

_____

_____

_____

_____

_____

_____

_____

_____

_____

_____

_____

_____

_____

_____

_____

_____

Tips & Suggestions:

RECIPE:

SERVES: _____   PREP TIME: _____

OVEN TEMP: _____   COOKING TIME: _____

INGREDIENTS:

_____   _____

_____   _____

_____   _____

_____   _____

_____   _____

Place your recipe photo here.

METHOD:

_____

_____

_____

_____

_____

_____

_____

Tips & Suggestions:

Place your recipe photo here.

RECIPE:

SERVES: _____   PREP TIME: _____

OVEN TEMP: _____   COOKING TIME: _____

INGREDIENTS:

_____   _____

_____   _____

_____   _____

_____   _____

_____   _____

_____   _____

_____   _____

METHOD:

_____

_____

_____

_____

_____

_____

_____

Tips & Suggestions:

RECIPE:

SERVES: _____   PREP TIME: _____

OVEN TEMP: _____ COOKING TIME: _____

INGREDIENTS:

_____   _____
_____   _____
_____   _____
_____   _____
_____   _____
_____   _____

Place your recipe photo here.

METHOD:

_____
_____
_____
_____
_____
_____
_____
_____
_____
_____
_____
_____
_____
_____
_____
_____
_____
_____
_____
_____
_____
_____
_____
_____

Tips & Suggestions:

RECIPE:

SERVES: _____   PREP TIME: _____

OVEN TEMP: _____   COOKING TIME: _____

INGREDIENTS:

_____   _____

_____   _____

_____   _____

_____   _____

_____   _____

_____   _____

METHOD:

_____

_____

_____

_____

_____

_____

_____

_____

_____

_____

_____

_____

_____

_____

_____

_____

_____

_____

_____

_____

_____

_____

Place your recipe photo here.

Tips & Suggestions:

RECIPE:

SERVES: _____ PREP TIME: _____

OVEN TEMP: _____ COOKING TIME: _____

INGREDIENTS:

_____ _____

_____ _____

_____ _____

_____ _____

_____ _____

_____ _____

Place your recipe photo here.

METHOD:

_____

_____

_____

_____

_____

_____

_____

_____

Tips & Suggestions:

RECIPE:

SERVES: _____ PREP TIME: _____

OVEN TEMP: _____ COOKING TIME: _____

INGREDIENTS:

_____ _____

_____ _____

_____ _____

_____ _____

_____ _____

METHOD:

_____

_____

_____

_____

_____

_____

_____

_____

_____

_____

_____

_____

_____

_____

_____

_____

_____

_____

_____

_____

Place your recipe
photo here.

Tips & Suggestions:

BREAD

Sourdough, soda bread, flatbread, corn bread, rye bread, wheat bread, buns and dumplings. Bread must be the most universally shared food in the world. The huge variety of possibilities is breathtaking and the pleasure and purpose in kneading warm, rising dough is the stuff of life. Who doesn't want to produce the perfect loaf?

Recipe Finder

Place your recipe photo here.

RECIPE:

SERVES: _____   PREP TIME: _____

OVEN TEMP: _____   COOKING TIME: _____

INGREDIENTS:

_____   _____

_____   _____

_____   _____

_____   _____

_____   _____

_____   _____

METHOD:

_____

_____

_____

_____

_____

_____

Tips & Suggestions:

RECIPE:

SERVES: _____   PREP TIME: _____

OVEN TEMP: _____   COOKING TIME: _____

INGREDIENTS:

_____   _____
_____   _____
_____   _____
_____   _____
_____   _____
_____   _____
_____   _____

Place your recipe photo here.

METHOD:

_____
_____
_____
_____
_____
_____
_____
_____
_____
_____
_____
_____
_____
_____
_____
_____
_____
_____
_____
_____
_____
_____
_____

Tips & Suggestions:

RECIPE:

SERVES: _____   PREP TIME: _____

OVEN TEMP: _____   COOKING TIME: _____

INGREDIENTS:

_____   _____

_____   _____

_____   _____

_____   _____

_____   _____

_____   _____

_____   _____

Place your recipe
photo here.

METHOD:

_____

_____

_____

_____

_____

_____

_____

_____

_____

_____

_____

_____

_____

_____

_____

_____

_____

_____

_____

_____

_____

Tips & Suggestions:

RECIPE:

SERVES: _____   PREP TIME: _____

OVEN TEMP: _____   COOKING TIME: _____

INGREDIENTS:

_____   _____

_____   _____

_____   _____

_____   _____

_____   _____

_____   _____

_____   _____

Place your recipe photo here.

METHOD:

_____

_____

_____

_____

_____

_____

_____

_____

_____

Tips & Suggestions:

Place your recipe photo here.

RECIPE:

SERVES: _____ PREP TIME: _____

OVEN TEMP: _____ COOKING TIME: _____

INGREDIENTS:

_____ _____

_____ _____

_____ _____

_____ _____

_____ _____

_____ _____

_____ _____

METHOD:

_____

_____

_____

_____

_____

_____

_____

_____

_____

Tips & Suggestions:

RECIPE:

SERVES: _____

OVEN TEMP: _____

PREP TIME: _____

COOKING TIME: _____

INGREDIENTS:

_____ _____

_____ _____

_____ _____

_____ _____

_____ _____

_____ _____

*Place your recipe
photo here.*

METHOD:

_____

_____

_____

_____

_____

_____

_____

_____

_____

_____

_____

_____

_____

_____

_____

_____

_____

_____

_____

_____

Tips & Suggestions:

RECIPE:

SERVES: _____ PREP TIME: _____

OVEN TEMP: _____ COOKING TIME: _____

INGREDIENTS:

_____ _____
_____ _____
_____ _____
_____ _____
_____ _____

Place your recipe photo here.

METHOD:

Tips & Suggestions:

JAMS AND PICKLES

Jellies and marmalades, pickles and chutneys, confits and curds. There's nothing like a glut of soft fruit or vegetables to prompt a jamfest! Cue a multitude of pots and pans, bottles and jars, accompanied by tireless stirring and testing. It may be a humble kitchen, but this is industrial! There's something very satisfying about preserving food today for sharing tomorrow.

Recipe Finder

Place your recipe photo here.

RECIPE:

SERVES: _____ PREP TIME: _____

OVEN TEMP: _____ COOKING TIME: _____

INGREDIENTS:

METHOD:

Tips & Suggestions:

RECIPE:

SERVES: _____ PREP TIME: _____

OVEN TEMP: _____ COOKING TIME: _____

INGREDIENTS:

METHOD:

Place your recipe
photo here.

Tips & Suggestions:

RECIPE:

SERVES: _____   PREP TIME: _____

OVEN TEMP: _____   COOKING TIME: _____

INGREDIENTS:

_____   _____

_____   _____

_____   _____

_____   _____

_____   _____

_____   _____

Place your recipe photo here.

METHOD:

_____

_____

_____

_____

_____

_____

_____

_____

_____

_____

_____

_____

_____

_____

_____

_____

_____

_____

_____

Tips & Suggestions:

RECIPE:

SERVES: _____   PREP TIME: _____

OVEN TEMP: _____   COOKING TIME: _____

INGREDIENTS:

_____   _____

_____   _____

_____   _____

_____   _____

_____   _____

Place your recipe photo here.

METHOD:

_____

_____

_____

_____

_____

_____

_____

Tips & Suggestions:

_____

Place your recipe photo here.

RECIPE:

SERVES: PREP TIME:

OVEN TEMP: COOKING TIME:

INGREDIENTS:

METHOD:

Tips & Suggestions:

RECIPE:

SERVES: _____ PREP TIME: _____

OVEN TEMP: _____ COOKING TIME: _____

INGREDIENTS:

_____ _____

_____ _____

_____ _____

_____ _____

_____ _____

METHOD:

_____

_____

_____

_____

_____

_____

_____

_____

_____

_____

_____

_____

_____

_____

_____

_____

_____

Place your recipe photo here.

Tips & Suggestions: